DIGGERS AND BUILDERS

BY HENRY LENT

DIGGERS AND BUILDERS

Stories of men who run derricks, trucks, steam shovels; who mix cement, build skyscrapers and make roads.

CLEAR TRACK AHEAD!

A "first" railroad book; all about the men who make the trains run safely, engineers, brakemen, conductors and others.

FULL STEAM AHEAD!

The story of six days on an ocean liner; exploring it from bridge to engine rooms.

Diggers
and
Builders

BY
HENRY LENT

PICTURES BY THE AUTHOR

New York
The Macmillan Company
1950

This book is for

_____

who, like Henry Jr. and David,
(inquisitive little scamps!)
must know *What, How* and *Why!*

CONTENTS

PAGE

TONY

THE STEAM SHOVEL MAN 1

SAM

THE CEMENT MIXER 13

DAN

THE DERRICK MAN 25

JOE

THE STEEL WORKER 37

PEDRO

THE ROAD BUILDER 51

BILL

THE TRUCK DRIVER 61

TONY

THE STEAM SHOVEL MAN

HIS is Tony, the man who runs the steam shovel. He wears a bright red handkerchief about his neck. He twirls his shiny black mustache and smiles. In one hand he carries his lunch box, full of good things to eat when the twelve o'clock whistle blows. It is a hard job to run a steam shovel, but Tony is very strong.

To-day Tony must dig out a great hole in the earth, so that other men can start to build a tall apartment house. This hole is called an "excavation." A big red truck, shining in the sunlight, is already starting to chug slowly down the steep wooden runway into the hole toward the steam shovel. This truck, and many others like it, will haul away the dirt as fast as the steam shovel can dig it up. They carry the dirt to the edge of the city, where they dump it and come back for more.

[3]

DIGGERS AND BUILDERS

It is still early in the morning when Tony walks down the runway and clambers up into the cab of his steam shovel. His helper shovels coal into the great boiler, for he must have a red-hot fire to make plenty of steam. Finally the steam hisses. Psss! Psss! The big shovel is ready to start work.

The steam shovel looks very much like a small house on wheels. At one end is the cab, or driver's place. Here are the levers which operate the shovel. At the other end is the big boiler with its smokestack sticking up through the roof. The shovel itself is really a huge bucket which scoops up more dirt than many men could dig up with their ordinary shovels. It takes only a few big bucketfuls of dirt to fill a large dump truck.

Now the red truck is down close to the steam shovel. Tony pulls a lever with his strong arms. The heavy iron bucket drops down. He pulls another lever. The big scoop digs into the earth. In a jiffy the bucket is heaping full. Then Tony presses a large pedal with his foot. The bucket rises high into the air.

Tony must watch very carefully now! He pulls another lever and the bucket swings slowly around, over the truck. When it is just right, the truck driver waves his hand. Quick as a wink, Tony jerks the cord, and plop! the bottom of the bucket opens and the dirt falls into the truck with a loud noise.

[6]

TONY—THE STEAM SHOVEL MAN

When the truck is loaded full with dirt and stones, the driver starts his engine, and the truck climbs up the steep planks out of the hole, to make room for the next truck. Chug . . . chug . . . chug . . . ever so slowly, for the truck has a heavy load.

Sometimes men walk behind the truck with big blocks of wood which they quickly slip under the wheels if the engine begins to sputter. This prevents the truck from rolling back into the hole.

All day long Tony pushes and pulls the big levers of his steam shovel. Bucketful after bucketful, the dirt comes up and is emptied into the trucks.

Finally the hole becomes so large that Tony must move the steam shovel forward, where there is more dirt to scoop up. Have you ever seen a steam shovel move? It rolls along slowly on little wheels that run along a big, flat sort of chain. Because it crawls

very much like a caterpillar, this is called a "caterpillar tread." The little wheels move the giant steam shovel quite easily, even up over bumps and rough places.

Tony's helper must keep shoveling coal into the boiler all day long to keep the fire burning hotly. In the boiler, directly over the hot fire, are pipes of water. As the fire burns fiercely, the water boils and turns into steam. Steam is very powerful. It drives the

[8]

pistons on huge railroad locomotives . . . and in Tony's steam shovel, the steam drives the pistons which turn the wheels and gears —and this is the machinery which makes the giant digger work. Black smoke pours out of the stack each time he shovels. Sometimes red sparks shoot up into the air.

For many days Tony and his hissing steam shovel dig and dig, deeper and deeper. At last he cannot even see up over the top of the steep sides of the hole his shovel has dug.

Finally, when there is no more dirt to be taken out, Tony jumps down from his cab and looks about him. He has dug a deep hole. But he is very wise. He knows exactly how to get out. Do you know how he does it?

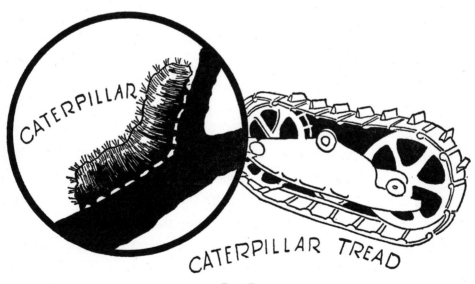

CATERPILLAR

CATERPILLAR TREAD

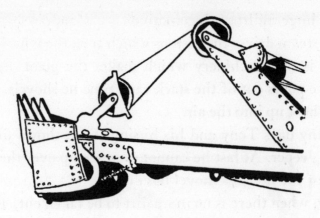

Tony walks up to the foreman. "We're ready to move, boss," he says. "If your men will give us a hand, we'll soon be out of here." The men carry heavy timbers over to the steam shovel. They lay them down close together so that they make a plank road leading right up to the steep runway that the trucks have been using. Everything is ready. Tony climbs back into his steam shovel. Now then, everybody must get out of the way!

What a puffing and snorting as the steam shovel starts to climb up, up, out of the hole! Sometimes it slips back a little, but Tony opens the throttle, turns on more steam, and it keeps on moving. When he reaches the top, Tony steers it right onto a big low trailer which is hitched to a truck. Then the truck driver tows Tony and his steam shovel away, to dig another hole somewhere else.

Every day, as Tony works, many people stop to watch him and his steam shovel. His hands are too busy to wave to the boys and

girls who watch him from the fence up above the hole, but Tony always has a smile. For he likes children.

Perhaps, some day, *you* will see Tony and his steam shovel digging.

SAM

THE CEMENT MIXER

ERE is Sam, the cement-mixer man. He wears a blue shirt and an old slouch hat, tilted back on his head. Sam knows everything there is to know about cement mixing, for he is boss of the cement workers. Now that Tony has finished digging the excavation, they can start working. Their job is to lay a thick, smooth floor in the large square hole, which will then become the cellar of the apartment house. They will also make cement walls . . . the foundations of the tall building.

"Come on, men! Everybody on the job!" shouts Sam, as he takes his place by the big cement mixer. One of the men cranks the gasoline engine that turns the mixer. Pop . . . poppity . . . pfft! It refuses to start. Once again he cranks it. This time it sputters and starts—pop . . . poppity-pop . . . chug . . . chug . . . chug. Now it is running at top speed. It is always a hard job to get cement mixers started.

DIGGERS AND BUILDERS

Two of Sam's helpers are wheelbarrow men. It is their job to keep the cement mixer full of sand and gravel. They have built a long narrow runway leading to the mixer from the big piles of sand and gravel which the dump trucks have left for them. One helper loads only sand in his wheelbarrow. The other helper brings loads of gravel to the mixer.

Piled on the ground near the mixer are many bags of cement. Cement is made in factories called "cement works." It is shipped

to builders in white cloth bags which weigh about one hundred pounds each. Cement is a very soft, dry powder. After it has been wet, and becomes dry again, cement turns into stone. That is why Sam covers up the bags very carefully at night, for it might rain. Even when a bag of cement becomes damp—and that often happens —it turns into big, hard lumps which must be broken up in the mixer.

Now they are starting. Sam holds the lever of the cement mixer firmly as the wheelbarrows come with their loads. Some mixers have a big scooplike affair called a hopper, attached to the side.

When the hopper is full, it raises up so that the material can slide down into the mixer. First a load of sand, then a load of gravel . . . another of sand and one more of gravel. That's the way it should go, says Sam! When the wheelbarrow men have each dumped two brimming loads in the mixer, Sam lifts a heavy sack of cement from the pile behind him and empties it into the cement mixer. Now the water man is dipping his bucket into the huge barrel that stands on the other side of the mixer. Into the mixer goes the water! It is full now. Round and round and round it goes, as the little engine chugs away. Be sure to let it mix long enough, Sam, so that all the hard lumps of cement get broken up.

Now and then, Sam turns the wheel on the side of the mixer. This lowers the mixer a little so he can look into it to see how the cement is mixing. It mustn't be too thick, for then it will not run down the sluiceway, or chute, which the carpenters have built. And if it is too thin and watery, it will not make good strong cement. In that case, Sam must add a little more sand and gravel.

When the cement is thoroughly mixed, Sam turns the wheel all the way round. This tilts the mixer downward. With a loud swishing noise the cement pours out of the mixer into the chute. On down the wooden chute it flows, and on to the flat dirt bottom of the great hole. Fast at first, then slower and slower. Sometimes if the cement doesn't go down the chute fast enough, Sam's helpers push it along with a small flat paddle, or board which is nailed to a pole.

As soon as the mixer is completely empty, Sam turns the wheel

again and the mixer tilts back, ready for another load. Once more the wheelbarrow men fill it with sand and gravel. Throw in the bag of cement, Sam! Pour in the water, water man! And the mixer turns round and round, swishing it all together.

Load after load pours out of the mixer into the chute. Finally Sam asks one of his helpers to run the cement mixer for him. He

must go down into the excavation to see how his men are doing their job as the cement comes to them down through the chute.

Sam is very much pleased with the way his helpers have been spreading the cement on the ground. It makes a nice thick layer, which some of the men are already smoothing off with a long

[20]

narrow board. He walks over to watch two other men, who are making a flat, smooth surface on the cement with their wide trowels. Cement hardens very quickly. If you should come back to-morrow morning, you would find it had become a hard, smooth floor that you could walk on. This floor will be the basement of the apartment building when it is finished. Other men will come later to set up a furnace and pipes with which the apartment can be heated in winter.

The cement workers must be very careful not to walk on the smooth floor until it becomes hard, for their footprints would spoil the cement. One day when Sam and his helpers were making a cement sidewalk, a little boy came with his dog to watch the men at work. Suddenly the dog ran across the soft cement which the men were smoothing. And what do you think happened? His little paws left deep marks in the cement which Sam's workers had to

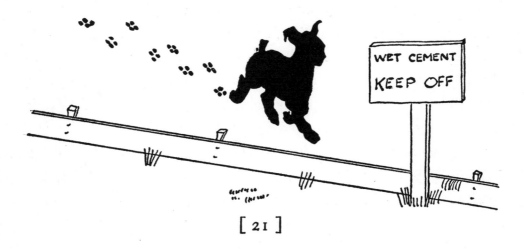

smooth all over again. The little dog, of course, did not know that the cement was soft.

Now the basement floor is finished, but Sam and his workers have another job to do before they leave. The basement of the apartment building must have cement walls. Walls are much easier than floors to build. The carpenters merely board up the sides of the excavation. This is called building a "form." The men move the chutes so that the cement which pours from the mixer dumps right into the forms. Then they leave it until it becomes hard. When the wooden forms are removed, there is the cement wall!

Sam and his cement workers have finished now. They are picking up their shovels and paddles. The water man is washing the inside of the cement mixer so it will be clean to start the next job. Soon a truck will come and tow it away.

In big cities it is not always necessary for Sam to bring his cement mixer to the excavation, for there are big trucks which have cement mixers behind the driver's cab. All day long these big cement-mixing trucks drive into the builders' supply yard, where the large central cement-mixing plant is located. As each truck backs up to the chute, the cement, already mixed, flows down into the huge mixing drum on the truck. One by one they leave the yard, headed for the building job that has ordered the cement. As they drive through the city streets, the mixer turns slowly, mixing the cement still more as it is being hauled to the excavation. When they reach the excavation, they back up to the chute, tilt the big mixer behind the driver's cab—and the cement pours down to the men who are waiting to spread it. This saves a great deal of time.

DAN

The Derrick Man

THE steam shovel and the cement mixer have finished their jobs and gone away. The deep, square hole is ready for the steel workers, who will soon start to erect the tall apartment building. Here comes Dan, the derrick man, with his crew of workmen. He climbs down quickly into the excavation, looking carefully about to decide just where his derrick can be set up. He must also find a good place for the heavy timbers on which the derrick engine and hoist must rest. In a few minutes Dan climbs back up the ladder to the street. "Everything is O.K.," he says.

Here comes the derrick, loaded piece by piece on a huge trailer which the truck is towing. Dan and his men leap into action. "Make it snappy, boys!" he shouts, as they start to unload the heavy steel sections of the derrick. The derrick cannot, of course, be towed through city streets until it has first been taken apart—for it is much too long.

DIGGERS AND BUILDERS

As soon as Dan's men have lifted all the sections of the derrick from the trailer, they fit them together and bolt them firmly with their long wrenches. Last of all, they unload the hoist, or engine, which runs the derrick. What a job *that* is! It is so heavy that they must first lay down thick timbers as a sort of chute, to slide it from the truck down to the ground.

Hurry up, Dan! The steel trucks will soon be here with the first load of girders, the great strong steel beams and upright pieces that make the skeleton or framework of the building. You'd better set up your derrick to unload them and hoist them into place!

Finally the derrick is set in place at the bottom of the great hole. Even then it rises so high into the sky that the top of it reaches way up over the street level. Strong, heavy steel cables are stretched from the tip of the derrick to each corner of the excavation, to hold it firm and rigid. Dan's helpers take their places. Each one knows his job. His chief helper is the hoist man who runs the engine down in the hole.

The first truck is here now, loaded high with long steel girders. The hoist man nods to Dan to tell him that he is ready to start. He has already tried his levers. He glances up now at the two thick wire cables which run from his hoist up to the top of the derrick. There is a large iron hook attached to the lower end of the cable.

Dan is standing at the edge of the hole by the big truck. He will be the signal man for a while, for some one must tell the hoist man when to raise and lower the hook. The hoist operator, you know,

cannot even see the load his derrick must lift, for he is way down in the excavation, out of sight.

Dan moves his hand from side to side. See, the boom of the derrick is swinging round slowly. The hook is coming down close to

the pile of girders. Quickly two of the men pass a wire rope under the girders and attach it to the hook. When it is fastened securely, Dan waves his hand again. The hoist man knows that is the signal to raise the load. He pulls another lever. Slowly the heavy pieces of steel rise up . . . up . . . into the air.

DIGGERS AND BUILDERS

When the girders are directly over the hole, the derrick swings slowly around. Little by little the load is lowered into the hole. When it reaches the ground, Dan's helpers slip the wire rope from the hook. Soon the steel workers will climb down to start building the framework of the apartment. Each girder that the derrick hoists into the hole has a mark on it. This mark shows exactly where the steel workers must place it. As each girder is lowered into place, the steel workers bolt it together quickly with great wrenches and hurry on to the next one. Later, other steel workers will remove the bolts and rivet the girders together.

All day long the big trucks rumble down the street with their heavy loads. And all day long the derrick is busy, unloading them.

The steel workers are busy, too, erecting the high framework of the building. Now it is three stories high. As fast as the building rises into the sky, Dan and his crew hoist the derrick itself up to the top. Now, instead of lowering steel beams into the hole, the derrick must lift them high up into the air. Every day the building becomes higher and higher, as the steel workers fasten together the beams which the derrick hoists up to them.

Finally the derrick is thirty stories above the ground. It appears to be very small, but that is because it is so high. Now the last truck has brought its load of girders. The derrick has lifted its last beam high into the air. The beam has been fastened in place by the steel workers. There is no more work for the derrick to do on this building.

DIGGERS AND BUILDERS

Dan and his men take the derrick apart. They lower each piece over the side of the building to the truck and trailer which are waiting below, way down on the street. Piece by piece it is loaded on to the trailer and then is towed away. Dan and his crew leave, too, for they must start to hoist steel beams for a new building in another part of the city.

Although the derrick which is used to hoist steel girders on a building is probably larger, there are many other types of powerful lifters which are really derricks. Have you ever been down to the docks, where the boats are loading up for their long voyages? They use a derrick too. Their derricks, however, are somewhat smaller than the one Dan uses. Even a small derrick is very powerful. Sometimes automobiles must be hoisted on to the boat. Heavy boxes and crates, too, are lifted very easily by the boat's derrick.

[34]

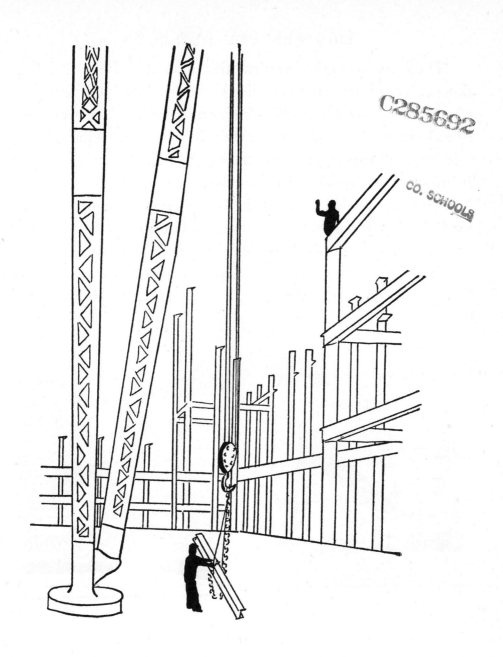

DIGGERS AND BUILDERS

There are also other derricks that look very much like steam shovels. They travel on wheels like the steam shovel, but in place of a bucket they have a hook. Wrecking cars on railroads, too, are really derricks mounted on flat cars. If there is an accident which causes a locomotive or cars to jump the tracks, the derrick flat-car rushes to it full speed, and quickly lifts them back on to the track.

Even the towing car, which the garage man uses, is really a small derrick. If the wheels of an automobile are broken, the towing car backs up to it, the hook of the derrick is fastened to the axle and lifts it off the ground so the garage man can easily tow it to his shop to fix it. A derrick, you will agree, is a very useful machine.

JOE

THE STEEL WORKER

OR many days big trucks have been hauling tons of heavy steel girders for the derrick to hoist up for the new apartment building. Now it is fifteen stories high above the street. Each day the black steel work rises up three or four stories higher. It will soon be finished. Let us watch the men whose job it is to join steel to steel—the men who rivet the girders together.

A rivet is a giant spike without a point. On one end it is flat, somewhat like the head of a nail. When Joe has done *his* work on each rivet, it is flat on both ends and holds the steel girders together securely.

Here is Joe, the steel worker. He is the rivet man. Joe has three helpers in his gang: the "heater," the "catcher," and the "bucker-up." They all wear heavy gloves to protect their hands. You will soon see why.

"All right, gang, let's go!" shouts Joe. The heater has already started his fire. He has a small furnace set up on boards which are stretched across the steel beams. With one hand he turns the furnace blower. Sparks fly up into the air as the fire becomes hotter and hotter. In his right hand he holds a pair of long tongs. Soon the fire is white-hot. The heater reaches with his tongs into the keg of steel rivets by his side, picks out a rivet and thrusts it into the hot fire. How the sparks fly about his hands as he turns the blower! In a minute the rivet, too, will be hot.

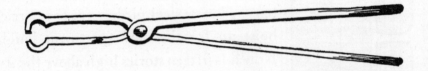

Over on the corner of the framework is Joe, with the other men in his gang, the catcher and the bucker-up. The derrick has already lowered a girder into place. The bolts have already been removed. The holes are lined up, ready for the rivets to be driven.

The catcher is standing on wooden planks which have been laid across the girders. He holds an iron bucket in his hand. Watch out, catcher! Here comes the rivet! Sure enough, the heater has lifted the red-hot rivet from the fire. He swings it with his tongs and lets it go. See how it flies through the air to the catcher man. Clank! right into the bucket. Quickly the catcher takes the hot rivet from the bucket with his tongs and sticks it into the hole in the girder. That

is why a catcher is sometimes called a "sticker." He not only catches the hot rivet but also must stick it into the hole.

"O.K.!" says Joe. Then . . . clackity-clack . . . clackity-clack! What a noise Joe makes with his rivet hammer! His helper,

the bucker-up, is leaning with all his strength against a short steel bar pressing against the other end of the rivet, while Joe hammers with his rivet "gun." The rivet gun, or hammer, can be heard many blocks away in the city. It is sometimes called a "cricket" because it sounds just like a giant cricket, "crickety-cricketing" way up in the steel framework. The rivet "gun" is driven by compressed air which is forced into it through a tough rubber hose. Soon the end of the rivet is flattened out. So much for *that* one!

The catcher has just caught another rivet from the heater. Quickly he sticks it in the next hole. The bucker-up presses his bar

against it. Joe places his heavy hammer against the other end. Clack-ity-clack . . . clackity-clack! Another rivet is in. Only two more holes to rivet and the girder will be securely fastened.

It is great fun to watch the heater throw the red-hot rivets to

the catcher. The bucket man must never miss the rivet as it shoots
through the air. Sometimes he has to lean way out over the girder

with his bucket as it whizzes toward him. Clank! It's in the bucket!
Clank! He's caught another rivet. So it goes, all day long.

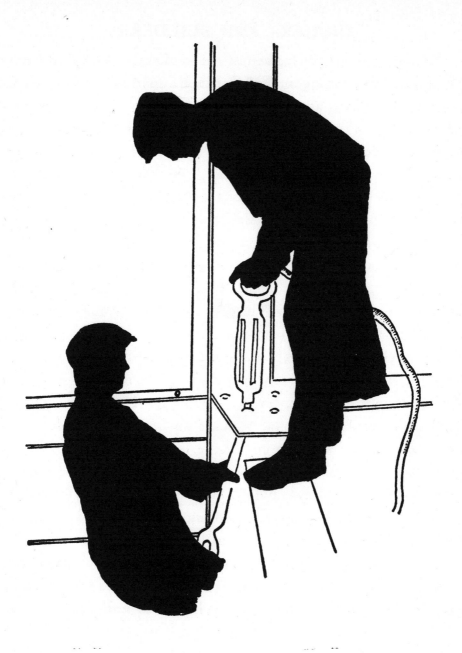

DIGGERS AND BUILDERS

Joe's job is really the hardest job of all. His arms must be strong to hold the heavy rivet gun. It makes such a loud noise that it is impossible to hear what anyone says. Perhaps, some day soon, the clattering rivet "gun" will be a thing of the past. The rivet, too, will no longer be needed. For men who know all about new ways of building say that it is possible to weld steel girders together at the joints, just as you make a candle stick to its holder by melting some of the wax. Then there will be no danger of red-hot rivets whizzing through the air, but instead there will be men with welding torches which shoot out their tiny blue and white flame to melt, or weld, the girders together at the joints. People who are annoyed by the clatter of the rivet "gun" will be glad, for welding makes no noise.

Steel workers are very sure-footed. See how carefully they balance themselves as they walk along the narrow steel girders. Sometimes Joe stops to rest while he is waiting for the next rivet. He looks down into the street, far, far below him. How tiny the automobiles and people seem to be from the top of a tall skyscraper! On clear days Joe can see way out in the harbor. He watches ocean liners steaming in past the Statute of Liberty. Little tugboats scurry to and fro like tiny water-spiders. Steel workers used to "ride" up on girders as the derrick hoisted them into the air. This is a dangerous thing to do and nowadays it is really against the rules.

Joe is very happy to-day. Before the five o'clock whistle blows, he and his gang will have the last steel girder riveted in place. As he drives in the final rivet, one of his helpers will hoist an American

flag at the top of the steel work. This means that the thirtieth story of the apartment building has been completed. That is as high as it must go.

The next time you see the steel framework of a skyscraper, look way up at the top. If the flag is fluttering in the breeze, you will know that Joe and his rivet gang have finished their work and gone away.

PEDRO

THE ROAD BUILDER

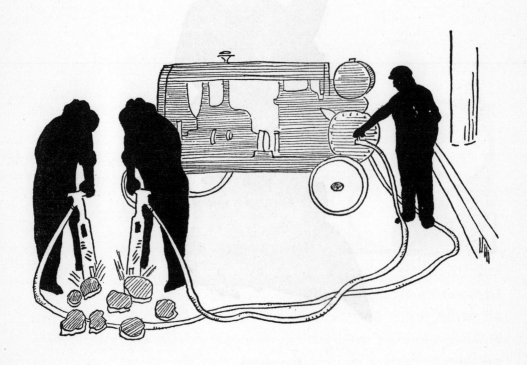

EE what's going on here! Out beyond the apartment building, at the edge of the city, Pedro and his crew of road builders are tearing up a long stretch of old road so they can build a smooth wide highway for us to drive on.

Rat-ta-ta-tat! Rat-ta-ta-tat! What a noise the drills make as they dig down into the hard dirt and stone! Compressed-air drills are driven just as the rivet "guns" are, by the air which rushes into them through a long rubber hose connected to an air-compressor machine. Sometimes the drills are called "road-breakers." Each drill does the work that five or six men would ordinarily do with only a pick, a hand drill, and a sledge hammer.

Pedro stands with his pipe in his mouth watching the drillers as they pry loose great slabs of the old pavement. Other men, with heavy sledge hammers, pound the slabs to break them into smaller pieces. Now and then they stop long enough to lift them up into a dump truck, which follows them as they work. When the truck is loaded full, it hauls away the stones and comes back empty for another load. Pedro is a good boss and his men work hard to please him.

When the digging crew has finished tearing up the old roadway, Pedro and his men mark out the new road very carefully with strings. As they go along they drive little stakes, or pegs, into the ground in a straight line. When they start to build the new road they must be sure to keep within these pegs, so that the edges will be perfectly straight. Pedro and his men have built many fine roads, and they know exactly how to do it.

Now Pedro is ready to start building the new road. This will be an asphalt road, a wide road, smooth and black. Have you ever heard the noise automobile tires make on a smooth asphalt road, especially if it is raining? Bzzzzzz! As they speed along.

All day long, since early morning, great trucks have been bringing loads of sand and gravel for Pedro and his workmen. They back up slowly, one at a time, and dump their loads in the roadway. First a layer of sand, then a layer of gravel. Each time a truck comes up, Pedro tells the driver where to dump it. Sometimes after the truck has tipped up its load of sand, some of the sand sticks to the bottom. Has this ever happened to your toy truck? Then Pedro hits the bottom of the truck with his sledge hammer, to jar the sand loose and start it sliding down, down, out on the ground. The gravel trucks dump their loads very easily, for small stones never stick together. What a rushing, rumbling noise they make as they pour out on to the ground!

As each truck drives away, Pedro's men spread the sand and gravel with their shovels, until it is quite smooth. That part of the

road they are making now is called a "roadbed." It must be packed down very hard. Can you guess how they do it, before I tell you?

"Out of the way, men!" shouts Pedro. Listen! You can hear something coming down the road . . . chug . . . chug . . . chug. Here comes the steam roller! What a big black machine it is! How it snorts and hisses steam as it comes lumbering along the rough road! The steam-roller man sits up on his little seat, steering the giant machine very much as you would steer an automobile. A steam roller, however, has only three wheels. The two rear wheels are very large, and the front wheel is really a big iron roller, as heavy as can be.

Very slowly the driver steers his steam roller over the sand and

gravel which Pedro's men have spread in the roadbed. It packs all this material very flat and smooth. Again and again it passes over the stones and sand, until it is almost as smooth as a wooden floor.

[56]

PEDRO—THE ROAD BUILDER

As the steam roller passes Pedro, he reaches for the step handle and climbs up on the seat beside the driver. Pedro used to be a steam-roller man himself. See, now he is taking the wheel. The steam-roller driver jumps down. Probably he is going to get a drink of water, for it is hot work, running a steam roller. Pedro drives the steam roller along the road, but he goes so slowly that the driver catches up to him and climbs back into the seat before he reaches the end of the pavement. Pedro climbs out, smiling. Running a steam roller is great fun, he says.

Late in the afternoon huge trucks can be seen coming down the road. But they are not dump trucks. These trucks have large tanks, very much like gasoline trucks. What do you think is in these great tanks? It is tar . . . black, sticky tar. This is the stuff that goes on top of the gravel and stones to make the smooth macadam highway. They have just been to the railroad siding where they have been filled from the huge tank cars which brought the tar from a distant city. Now watch how they put it on.

At the back of the tank truck there is a sort of sprinkler. As the truck drives over the roadbed, the driver turns the valve. Out comes the black tar, pouring thickly onto the road. As the truck passes, two men walk along the side of the road, scattering shovelfuls of very fine gravel over the tar.

When this has been done, the steam-roller man runs his machine over the road, packing it down into a hard, smooth surface.

DIGGERS AND BUILDERS

The road is finished. Pedro and his men load their tools into one of the trucks and drive off to build another road somewhere else.

Some time when you are riding in your car, you may come to a

sign in the road that says, *"DETOUR—MEN WORKING AHEAD"*. When that happens, you must take a side road, because cars cannot drive where Pedro and his workmen are busy making a

new road. Each night when they are through working, they hang a red lantern on the sign, so that it can be seen in the dark. The next time you drive that way, perhaps you will see no sign across the road. That means that Pedro has finished the road.

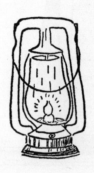

BILL

THE TRUCK DRIVER

IG trucks . . . little trucks . . . red trucks . . . yellow trucks . . . dump trucks . . . and trucks with trailers. If diggers and builders had no trucks to haul their supplies, it would be very difficult for them to do their jobs. Let us see just how the truck helps the men who build things.

Here is Bill, the truck driver. He wears a hat with a broad brim to keep the sun out of his eyes. On his feet are heavy driving boots that lace way up to his knees. Sometimes he wears gloves, or gauntlets, so that he can grasp the steering wheel firmly. Bill is very cheerful. He grins at the traffic policeman and whistles a tune as he drives through the city streets.

To-day Bill is driving a five-ton dump truck. He must haul away the dirt which Tony is scooping up with his steam shovel. When he comes to the steep plank roadway which leads down into the excavation where the steam shovel is digging, Bill shifts his truck into low gear. This acts as a sort of brake to prevent him from going down the incline too fast. Then he backs his truck under the steam-shovel bucket, which dumps great piles of dirt into it.

While he is waiting for the steam shovel to load his truck, Bill strolls over for a talk with Tony's helper. He keeps his eye on the truck, however, for there is no time to waste. He must haul many loads to-day. As soon as the last bucketful has been emptied into the truck, he runs over and climbs into the driver's seat. He starts his engine, and chugs slowly up the steep roadway with his heavy load.

It happens to-day that Pedro, the road builder, is digging out the roadbed for the new highway. Bill knows that he needs sandy dirt to fill it in for the steam roller to smooth off. So here he goes, chug, chug, chug, through the crowded streets, out to the edge of the city where Pedro is working. He dumps the dirt where Pedro wants it, and starts back to get another load.

Sometimes Bill drives a truck with a long trailer on which he carries the derrick for Dan, and heavy steel girders and beams for Joe, the steel worker. With such a long, hanging-over sort of load,

[64]

Bill must be very careful when he turns corners. He must tie a red flag on the end, too, so that other cars will not bump into the girders. This flag means *"Danger! Don't Come Too Close!"*

To-day Bill is driving a small dump truck filled with gravel and sand for Sam, the cement-mixer man. The truck is divided in half by a partition, or dividing board. One half is filled with gravel . . . the other with sand. On this truck, the body dumps its load from the side instead of the back.

Sam sees the truck coming down the street.

"Hurry up, Bill!" he shouts. "My men are almost out of sand and gravel to put in the cement mixer."

"Here it is, Sam!" replies Bill, and he stops so suddenly by the men with the wheelbarrows that his brakes make a squeaking noise. Out pours the sand . . . swish! Then the gravel . . . and he's off to get another load. Bill is very busy to-day!

When the workmen have finished building the tall apartment building, Bill has still another job. He uses a helper now, for he is a moving man. They pile all sorts of furniture into their huge moving van . . . chairs, tables, refrigerators, rugs, and all the other things people need in their apartments. The inside of the van is padded so that fine furniture will not become scratched. After the van is packed full, the helper jumps up on the seat beside Bill, and off they go to the apartment. On very big moving jobs, Bill sometimes uses three helpers. There is room for them all on the driver's seat, for moving vans are large and have very wide seats.

DIGGERS AND BUILDERS

Every night, after five o'clock, when Bill's work is done for the day, he drives his truck back to the garage, which is filled with all

kinds of trucks. Here there are mechanics, who work all night, while the truck drivers are sleeping. If there is anything that needs fixing, out come their wrenches and pliers! They inspect each truck carefully. Perhaps the tires need air—unless, as on some trucks, the tires are solid rubber tires. They clean the spark-plugs, adjust the

carburetor, and tighten all the nuts and bolts. In the morning Bill will find his truck in perfect running order.

The next time you are driving in the city and have to stop when

DIGGERS AND BUILDERS

the red traffic light flashes on, Bill the truck driver may stop his truck right beside your car to wait for the green light. And perhaps, if you wave to him, he will smile and wave to *you!*